Code

Into the Cave

Tony Bradman • **Jon Stuart**

Contents

OXFORD
UNIVERSITY PRESS

Macro Marvel
(billionaire inventor)

Welcome to Micro World!

Macro Marvel invented Micro World – a micro-sized theme park where you have to shrink to get in.

A computer called *CODE* controls Micro World and all the robots inside – MITEs and BITEs.

A MITE

A BITE

Disaster strikes!

CODE goes wrong on opening day.
CODE wants to shrink the world.

Macro Marvel is trapped inside the park …

Enter Team X!

Four micro agents – **Max, Cat, Ant** and **Tiger** – are sent to rescue Macro Marvel and defeat CODE.

Mini Marvel joins Team X.

Mini Marvel
(Macro's daughter)

In the last book ...

* Tiger trained a dragon to fly him over the Dragon Quest zone.

* Tiger lost control of the dragon, but Cat saved him.

**CODE key
(2 collected)**

You are in the Dragon Quest zone.

Before you read

Sound checker
Say the sounds.

a-e   ay
a

Sound spotter
Blend the sounds.

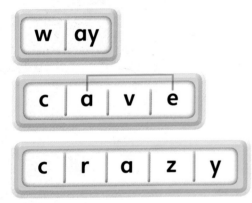

w	ay

c	a	v	e

c	r	a	z	y

Tricky word
one

Into the zone

How do you think Max, Ant and Mini might find the CODE key?

4

Dragon Eggs

Max, Ant and Mini stopped the jeep. They got out to look for the CODE key.

Max found some tracks.
"Come this way," he said.
"Wait for us!" shouted Ant.

They came to a cave.
The BITE was in the way.
"The CODE key must be in there,"
said Mini.

"It's crazy to go in the cave," said Mini.

"It's safe," said Ant. "The BITE is asleep."

They crept into the cave.

"Wow!" said Ant.
"The eggs are amazing.
Look at the big one!"

They did not see the BITE
wake up.

Now you have read ...
Dragon Eggs

Text checker

What do we know that
Max, Ant and Mini
don't know?

MITE fun

What do you think the Dragon-BITE
will do when it sees Max, Ant
and Mini?

Go back to sleep.

Fly away.

Attack.

Before you read

Sound checker
Say the sounds.

a-e   ay

a

Sound spotter
Blend the sounds.

| r | ay |

| b | a | b | y |

| a | w | a | k | e |

| f | l | a | m | e | s |

Tricky words
one
little
your

Into the zone
What kit do you think Team X
will use to help them find
the CODE key?

12

The Baby Dragon

"The CODE key might be in this cave," said Mini.

Ant looked in the eggs with his X-ray glasses.

"The baby dragon in that one has the CODE key!" said Ant.

Max tapped the egg but it only cracked a little bit.

Then Mini saw the BITE.
"The BITE is awake!" she cried.

The BITE shot flames at them. "Max, use your force shield," shouted Ant.

"I'll shrink to get in the egg and get the CODE key," said Ant.

Ant found the CODE key but he was too little to get it out.

Ant grew bigger and got the CODE key. The BITE shut down.

Snorp!

"I will take you with me," said Mini. "Your name can be Rex."

The baby dragon flicked its tail.

They made their way to the exit.
Ant put in the CODE key.

Now you have read ...
The Baby Dragon

To get to the next zone we have to read the CODE words. Then the exit door will open. Can you help us read them?

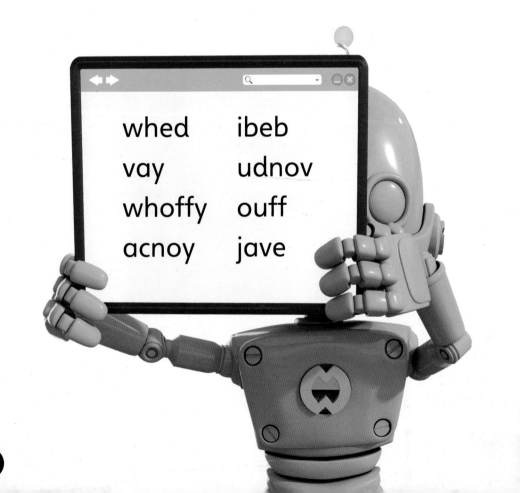

whed   ibeb

vay   udnov

whoffy   ouff

acnoy   jave